Contents

Choose the correct answer to each question and write it out.

1 Where is the baby playing?

   a) **The baby is playing in the playhouse.**

   b) **The baby is playing on the swing.**

2 Who is pushing the girl on the swing?

   a) **The boy is pushing the girl on the swing.**

   b) **Mum is pushing the girl on the swing.**

3 How many children are on the roundabout?

   a) **There are two children on the roundabout.**

   b) **There are three children on the roundabout.**

4 Where is the dog sitting?

   a) **The dog is sitting by the gate.**

   b) **The dog is sitting by the playhouse.**

5 Where is the football?

   a) **The football is under the see-saw.**

   b) **The football is under the slide.**

unit 2 The new house

Jenny has moved to a new house.

The front of the house has a red door. There is a window on each side of the door. There are two windows upstairs. There are blue curtains at all the windows.

Jenny's cat is sitting on the doorstep outside the front door.

Draw and colour Jenny's house.

4

The badger

A badger digs a home under the ground with its strong legs.

Its home has got many rooms and tunnels. The badger comes out at night to feed and play.

It likes to eat worms and insects.

Write out the sentence from each pair that is true.

1 a) **A badger lives in a tree.**
   b) **A badger lives under the ground.**

2 a) **A badger is awake at night.**
   b) **A badger is awake in the daytime.**

3 a) **A badger digs with its nose.**
   b) **A badger digs with its strong legs.**

4 a) **A badger likes to eat leaves.**
   b) **A badger likes to eat worms.**

The fox and the crow

One day a crow found some cheese and flew into a tree. A hungry fox saw him. He wanted the cheese for himself.

"You are a very beautiful bird and you have a very beautiful voice," said the fox. The crow was very pleased.

"Let me hear your beautiful voice. Sing to me," said the fox.

So the crow opened his beak and sang. The cheese fell down. The fox jumped up and caught the cheese.

Clever fox! Silly crow!

Choose the correct word to complete the sentences.

1 A crow had some ＿＿＿＿＿ in his beak.
cheese   food

2 A hungry ＿＿＿＿＿ saw him in the tree.
crow   fox

3 "You have a very ＿＿＿＿＿ voice," said the fox.
beautiful   loud

4 When the crow sang he opened his ＿＿＿＿＿.
eyes   beak

5 The fox ＿＿＿＿＿ the cheese as it fell down.
caught   dropped

Jack's birthday party

Choose the correct answer to each question and write it out.

1 How old is Jack?
   a) **Jack is seven.**
   b) **Jack is six.**

2 How many children did Jack invite to the party?
   a) **Jack invited six children to the party.**
   b) **Jack invited four children to the party.**

3 Where are they having tea?
   a) **They are having tea in Jack's bedroom.**
   b) **They are having tea in the kitchen.**

4 Who do you think is holding the cake?
   a) **I think Jack's mum is holding the cake.**
   b) **I think Jack's teacher is holding the cake.**

unit 6 Jenny's baby brother

Jenny had a baby brother and she didn't like him much. He was round and dimpled and lolled around the floor most of the time.

He was alright if you just wanted something soft to prod or cuddle but he wasn't much fun.

He was good at gurgling and sleeping and making a mess when he had his dinner. But there wasn't much you could really do with him.

"When is he going to be old enough to play with?" Jenny asked her mother.

But her mother just poked another spoonful of porridge into her brother's mouth and said, "I think he's lovely just as he is."

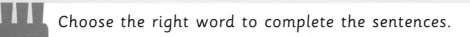

Choose the right word to complete the sentences.

1 Jenny had a baby _____ .
brother   doll

2 Jenny thought her baby brother was _____ .
fun   boring

3 Her brother made a mess at _____ .
dinner time   bedtime

4 Jenny wanted to _____ with her baby brother.
dance   play

5 Jenny's mother _____ him just as he is.
likes   doesn't like

unit 7

The missing sock

I found my sock
beneath the bed.
"Where have you been
all week?" I said.

"Hiding away,"
the sock replied.
"Another day on your foot
and I would have died!"

Choose the correct words to complete the sentences.

1 The boy found _____ .
a shoe   **a sock**

2 He found it _____ .
under his bed   **in his desk.**

3 The sock was missing for _____ .
a month   **a week**

4 I think the boy had _____ .
smelly feet   **clean feet**

How to make a mask

1

2

3

4

Write out the sentences in the correct order to explain what to do. Use the pictures to help you.

Cut out two eyeholes so you can see.

Put on the mask and surprise your friend.

Get a big brown paper bag.

Now draw a nose and mouth.

unit 9

Big Dog and Little Dog visit the moon

One night, when Big Dog and Little Dog were going home, they saw the moon in the sky. He was big and yellow, but he looked sad. "Poor Moon," said Little Dog.

Big Dog and Little Dog went home and made plans to build a rocket.

They would fly to the moon. Big Dog did lots of drawings. Little Dog coloured them in. They made a list.

Big Dog took all the money from their Piggy Bank. He gave it to Little Dog. Little Dog went shopping and bought the things they needed.

When Little Dog got back, Big Dog checked the shopping. There was: cardboard, string, sticky tape, wallpaper paste, elastic bands, plasticine and paint.

Write out the sentences and fill in the missing words.

1 Where were Big Dog and Little Dog going when they saw the moon?
Big Dog and Little Dog _____ .

2 How did they think the moon looked?
They thought the moon looked _____ .

3 Where did they plan to fly?
They planned to fly _____ .

4 What did they want the list of things for?
They wanted the things to make _____ .

5 Who bought the things for the rocket?
_____ **Dog bought the things for the rocket.**

Friends again

My brother bashed me with a stick.
I hit him with the hose.
He pulled my hair. I scratched his face.
He thumped me on the nose.

I bit his leg. He screamed. I screamed.
We called each other names.
Then Mum came out and asked us why
we couldn't play nice games.

I sulked. He moped. I frowned. He smiled.
I let him in my den.
He offered me a sticky sweet.
And now we're friends again.

Answer in sentences.
The answers have been started for you.

1 How many children are in this poem?
There are . . .

2 What was the brother hit with?
The brother was hit with . . .

3 What did the children call each other?
The children called each other . . .

4 Why did Mum come out?
Mum came out because . . .

5 Do you think the children were playing in the house or in the garden?
I think the children were playing . . .

The incredible shrinking hippo

It was Sunday when Simon found the hippopotamus. It looked like a big grey rock in the middle of the lawn.

"What are you doing here?" he asked.

"Looking for some mud," said the hippopotamus.

"There's no mud in our garden," said Simon. "I could put some water in the bath and you could splash around in that, but you're too big."

"Oh, that's no problem," said the hippo. "I can shrink. Just say the word 'tiny'."

"Tiny," said Simon.

The hippo got smaller and smaller until Simon could hold him in the palm of his hand.

"Brilliant!" laughed Simon. "You can be my pet now!"

Choose the correct answer to each question
and write it out.

1 When did Simon find the hippopotamus?

a) **Simon found the hippopotamus on Sunday.**

b) **Simon found the hippopotamus on Saturday.**

2 What was the hippopotamus looking for?

a) **The hippopotamus was looking for some food.**

b) **The hippopotamus was looking for some mud.**

3 What did the hippopotamus do when Simon said "tiny"?

a) **The hippopotamus got taller and taller.**

b) **The hippopotamus got smaller and smaller.**

4 What did Simon want the hippopotamus to be?

a) **Simon wanted it to be his pet.**

b) **Simon wanted it to be a secret.**

Making a windmill

Draw a square on a thick piece of coloured paper. Make each side 20 cms long.

Cut out the square.

Draw lines from corner to corner across the middle of the square. Cut along these lines from the corners for 10 cms.

Fold every other piece of corner to the middle of the paper.

Push a pin through the corners to fasten them together.

Push the pin into a long stick. Leave a space for the windmill to spin.

Write the captions in the correct order to make a windmill.

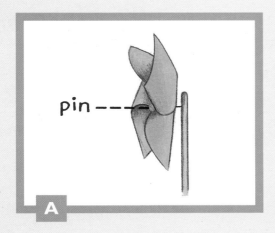

A

Push the pin into a stick.

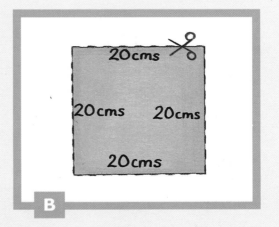

B

**Draw a square.
Cut it out.**

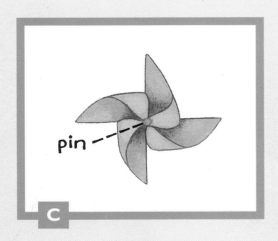

C

Fold every other corner to the middle. Fasten with a pin.

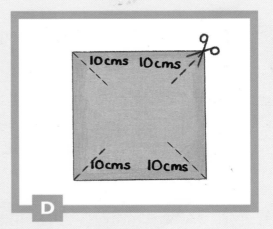

D

Cut along the lines for 10 cms.

unit 13   A jumble sale

The **Barton Playgroup** are having a **Jumble Sale** on Saturday, 16th November at 2 o'clock in the Village Hall. Your jumble, books and toys will be welcome.

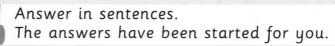

Answer in sentences.
The answers have been started for you.

1   Where is the jumble sale going to be?
The jumble sale is going to be . . .

2   What time does the jumble sale start?
The jumble sale starts . . .

3   What day is the jumble sale?
The jumble sale is . . .

4   What can you buy at a jumble sale?
You can buy . . .

unit 14

A party invitation

Dear **Ben**,

Please come to my party on Friday, 31st October.
The party will be in the Village Hall. It will start at
4 o'clock and finish at 7 o'clock. A magician is coming after tea.
He is called Mr Magic. Please let me know if you can come.

Love, *Tom*

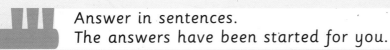

Answer in sentences.
The answers have been started for you.

1 Who has Tom invited to his party?
Tom has invited . . .

2 What time does the party start?
The party starts at . . .

3 Where is the party going to be?
The party is going to be in . . .

4 When is Mr Magic the magician coming?
Mr Magic the magician is coming . . .

5 What time should Ben's mum come to take
him home?
Ben's mum should come at . . .

Mrs Wobble the waitress

Mrs Wobble was a waitress. She liked her work. The customers liked her. The trouble was — she wobbled.

One day Mrs Wobble wobbled with a bowl of soup. The soup landed on a customer's dog. Mrs Wobble got told off.

The next day Mrs Wobble wobbled with a roast chicken. The roast chicken landed on a customer's head. Mrs Wobble got told off again.

The next day Mrs Wobble wobbled with a plate of jelly. The jelly landed on the *manager's* head. Mrs Wobble got the sack.

Answer in sentences.
The answers have been started for you.

1 What was Mrs Wobble's job?
Mrs Wobble's job was...

2 What was the trouble with Mrs Wobble?
The trouble with Mrs Wobble was...

3 Where did the roast chicken land?
The roast chicken landed...

4 Why did Mrs Wobble get the sack?
Mrs Wobble got the sack because...

5 Which food that Mrs Wobble carried is wobbly?
The wobbly food is...

unit 16 Stanley

A long time ago there were no houses and people lived in caves.

Stanley lived in a cave, but he did not like it. The cave was cold. So Stanley was cold. His head hurt because he had to sleep with it on a rock. Bats flew about as though they owned the place.

"Why can't we find a better way to live?" asked Stanley.

"This is good enough for us," said the other cavemen. "Why isn't it good enough for you?"

Answer in sentences.
The answers have been started for you.

1 What did people live in a long time ago?
People lived in . . .

2 Why didn't Stanley like where he lived?
Stanley didn't like where he lived because . . .

3 Why did the rock make Stanley's head hurt?
The rock made Stanley's head hurt because . . .

4 What did Stanley want to do?
Stanley wanted to find . . .

5 What do you think Stanley would like most about your house?
I think Stanley would like . . .

The rabbit

Rabbits have soft fur.
They have long ears.
Their back legs are big
and strong.

They have a little
white tail that bobs up
and down when they
hop about.

When danger is near,
a rabbit will hop down
its hole. Its bobbing tail
tells other rabbits about
the danger.

Rabbits dig tunnels under the ground to sleep in.

They like to eat grass and young plants.

Rabbits have two or three families every year. The babies are called kittens.

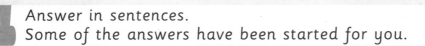

Answer in sentences.
Some of the answers have been started for you.

1 What are rabbits' ears like?
Rabbits' ears are . . .

2 What bobs up and down when a rabbit hops about?
The rabbit's . . .

3 Where do rabbits sleep?

4 What do rabbits eat?

5 What are baby rabbits called?

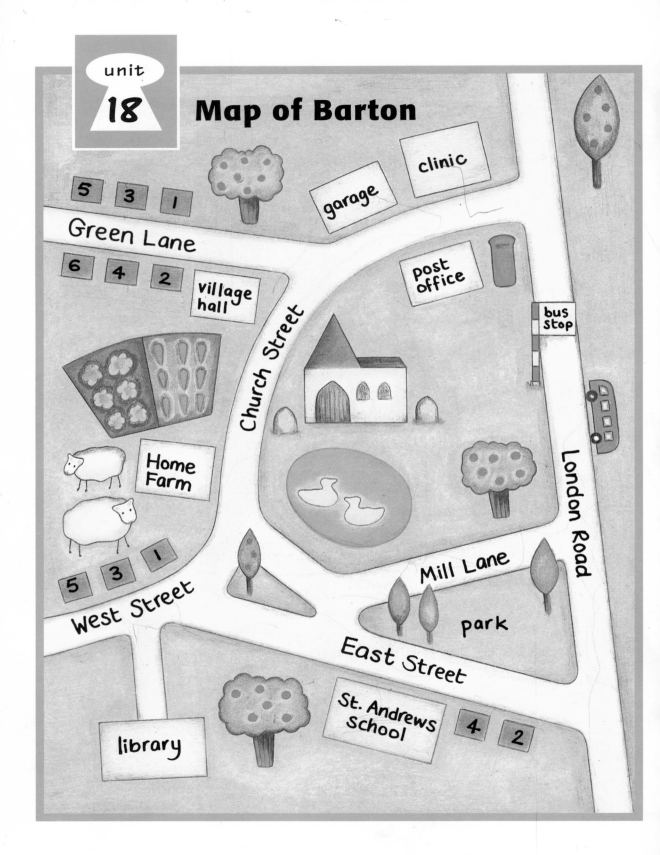

Answer in sentences.

1 Is there a library in Barton?

2 What is the farm called?

3 Where is the school?

4 How many houses are there in Green Lane?

5 Which street is the church in?

Enough

I've eaten all my vegetables.
Do I have to _____ my meat?
I'm strong enough already.
Can't I _____ down from my seat?

I have eaten all my cabbage.
I have _____ every pea.
I have eaten my potatoes.
There's no room left in _____ .

I've already grown _____ muscles.
I'm as fat as any tree.
So do I _____ to eat my meat
When I'm tall enough for me?

 Write out the poem and fill in the missing words.

get   have   me   eat   some   eaten